Functional Skills
Maths
Entry Level 3

This incredible CGP book is ideal for Entry Level 3 Functional Skills Maths practice. It covers all the major test providers, including Edexcel and City & Guilds.

There are 10-Minute Tests with questions on every topic, along with tests focused on non-calculator skills and mixed practice. We've also included easy-to-mark answers and a progress chart to track areas where students need extra support.

CGP — still the best! ☺

Our sole aim here at CGP is to produce the highest quality books — carefully written, immaculately presented and dangerously close to being funny.

Then we work our socks off to get them out to you — at the cheapest possible prices.

Contents

Section Four — Mixed Practice

Published by CGP

Editors:
Michael Bushell, Tom Miles, Rosa Roberts and Michael Weynberg

With thanks to Kevin Bennett and Glenn Rogers for the proofreading.

ISBN: 978 1 78908 568 6

Printed by Elanders Ltd, Newcastle upon Tyne.

Clipart from Corel®

Number: Test 1

1 Which of these numbers is the largest?

Tick (✓) your answer.

☐ 379

☐ 386

☐ 355

☐ 368   **[1]**

2 Which of these fractions is equivalent to $\frac{5}{10}$?

Tick (✓) your answer.

☐ $\frac{1}{2}$

☐ $\frac{2}{5}$

☐ $\frac{1}{5}$

☐ $\frac{5}{2}$ **[1]**

3 Work out 7×32.

....   **[1]**

4   Joanna has saved up a total of £372 to spend while on holiday.
She will spend the same amount on each of the 6 days that she is away.

How much will she spend each day?

£ ....   **[2]**

5   Joanna will travel by train and then by plane to her holiday destination:

Train
339 miles

Plane
514 miles

After travelling 100 miles, she thinks that she has less than 749 miles to go.
Is she correct? Show your working.

Tick (✓) your answer.   ☐ Yes   ☐ No   **[3]**

END OF TEST

/ 8

Number: Test 2

There are **5 questions** in this test.
Give yourself **10 minutes** to answer them all.
You **may** use a calculator for this test.

1   What is 956 in words?

Tick (✓) your answer.

☐   ninety-five hundred and six

☐   nine and fifty-six

☐   nine hundred and fifty-six

☐   nine hundred and sixty-five   **[1]**

2   Which of these lists of numbers is in order from largest to smallest?

Tick (✓) your answer.

☐   4.12   4.21   2.41

☐   2.41   4.12   4.21

☐   4.21   4.12   2.41

☐   4.21   2.41   4.12   **[1]**

3   A tech company has 427 employees.
How many is this to the nearest 10?

.... employees   **[1]**

---

4   The tech company makes tablet computers.
These are the heights of their different models:

Pocket	Small	Medium	Large	Super
13 cm	17 cm	21 cm	....	....

The heights follow a pattern.
Write in the missing heights to complete the table. **[2]**

5   The tech company hires 24 people to each test 15 tablets.

(a) How many tablets will these people test in total?

.... tablets **[1]**

(b) 180 of the tested tablets are reported to be broken.
$\frac{1}{10}$ of the broken tablets could **not** be fixed. The rest were fixed.
How many of the broken tablets were fixed?

.... tablets **[2]**

END OF TEST

/ 8

Number: Test 3

There are **5 questions** in this test.
Give yourself **10 minutes** to answer them all.
You **may not** use a calculator for this test.

1 What is 5 × 13?

Tick (✓) your answer.

☐ 60

☐ 65

☐ 70

☐ 75 **[1]**

2 Which of these numbers is the smallest?

Tick (✓) your answer.

☐ 5.38

☐ 5.83

☐ 5.36

☐ 5.82 **[1]**

3 Two out of five cars at a taxi company are coloured blue.
What fraction of the cars are **not** coloured blue?

☐
——
☐ **[1]**

4   Kyle drives for the taxi company. All drivers have to follow this rule:

> After 359 minutes of driving, you must take a break.

He has been driving for 61 minutes.

(a) How much longer is he allowed to drive before he must take a break?

.... minutes   [2]

(b) In the box below, use estimation to check your answer to part (a).

[1]

5   Kyle's taxi needs new tyres.

- It will cost £392 for a set of 4 tyres.
- Each tyre costs the same.

How much does one tyre cost?

£ ....   [2]

END OF TEST

/ 8

Number: Test 4

There are **5 questions** in this test.
Give yourself **10 minutes** to answer them all.
You **may** use a calculator for this test.

1 What is 975 rounded to the nearest 10?

Tick (✓) your answer.

☐ 900

☐ 970

☐ 980

☐ 1000 **[1]**

2 What is $\frac{1}{5}$ of 660 kg?

Tick (✓) your answer.

☐ 110 kg

☐ 132 kg

☐ 165 kg

☐ 330 kg **[1]**

3 Write the number 317 in words.

.... **[1]**

4   A school is selling tickets for their play.
The audience is split into 8 rows of 9 seats.

Romeo and Juliet
£13 per ticket

(a) What is the largest amount of money that the school
could raise from the ticket sales of one performance?

£ .... **[2]**

(b) The school raised £845 from the ticket sales of its first performance.
How many tickets were unsold for this performance?

.... tickets **[2]**

5   Five people will be asked to give feedback on the play.
The seat numbers of those who will be asked follow a pattern.

The first four seat numbers are 5, 19, 33 and 47.

Valerie is sitting in seat number 59.
Will she be asked to give feedback? Show your working.

Tick (✓) your answer.   ☐ Yes   ☐ No   **[1]**

END OF TEST

/ 8

Number: Test 5

There are **4 questions** in this test.
Give yourself **10 minutes** to answer them all.
You **may not** use a calculator for this test.

1   Which one of these fractions is **not** equivalent to $\frac{3}{4}$?

Tick (✓) your answer.

☐ $\frac{6}{8}$ ☐ $\frac{9}{12}$ ☐ $\frac{9}{16}$ ☐ $\frac{15}{20}$ **[1]**

2   Saanvi is furnishing a new apartment.
What is the total cost of the items on this receipt?

Tick (✓) your answer.

☐ £455

☐ £460

☐ £465

☐ £470

Furniture Store
26/03/2020   03:22 PM
Server: Tim
Rug.....................£190
Cushions...........£160
Lamp..................£115
Total:

[1]

3   A collection of paintings have the following prices.

| £334 | £316 | £326 | £342 | £314 | £321 | £320 |

Round the cost of the cheapest painting to the nearest £10.

£ ....   **[1]**

---

4   Saanvi is buying curtains. The curtains are available in store
in four lengths: 1.92 m, 2.00 m, 2.08 m and 2.16 m.

(a)   Saanvi doesn't want the curtains to touch the floor.
When hung, the distance between the top of
the curtains and the floor will be 2.05 m.

What is the length of the longest set of curtains that she can buy?

.... m   **[1]**

(b)   Curtain hooks are sold in boxes of 28.
There are 14 boxes of curtain hooks on a shelf.

How many curtain hooks are on the shelf in total?

.... hooks   **[2]**

(c)   Longer curtains can be bought by special order.
The lengths of all of the curtains follow a pattern.

What are the lengths of the next two sets of curtains?

.... m   .... m   **[2]**

END OF TEST

/ 8

Number: Test 6

There are **5 questions** in this test.
Give yourself **10 minutes** to answer them all.
You **may** use a calculator for this test.

1 What is the difference between 412 and 179?

Tick (✓) your answer.

☐ 591

☐ 224

☐ 233

☐ 242   **[1]**

2 What is 579 rounded to the nearest 100?

Tick (✓) your answer.

☐ 500

☐ 570

☐ 580

☐ 600   **[1]**

3 624 ÷ 53 =

.... remainder ....   **[1]**

---

4   Micah collects a magazine. The special issues are numbered in a pattern:

231   256   281   306

How many ordinary issues are there between each pair of special issues?

.... ordinary issues   **[1]**

5   The magazine costs £5 per issue. Micah plans to order 24 issues.

(a) How much would his order cost?

£ ....   **[1]**

(b) Micah can use one of the following offers.

Offer A   **Offer B**

$\frac{1}{4}$ off the cost   First 5 issues are free

Which offer saves Micah more money? Show your working.

Tick (✓) your answer.   ☐ Offer A   ☐ Offer B   **[3]**

END OF TEST

/ 8

Number: Test 7

There are **5 questions** in this test.
Give yourself **10 minutes** to answer them all.
You **may not** use a calculator for this test.

1 Which of these numbers is the smallest?

Tick (✓) your answer.

☐ 164.79

☐ 164.9

☐ 164.97

☐ 165.7   **[1]**

2 What number comes next in this sequence?   12.1   14.2   16.3   18.4

Tick (✓) your answer.

☐ 20.4

☐ 22.4

☐ 20.5

☐ 22.5   **[1]**

3 Use rounding to estimate the answer to 21 × 39.

....   **[1]**

4 Adele hosted a party. 3 people that were invited didn't attend.

This was $\frac{1}{10}$ of all the people that were invited.

How many of those invited **did** attend Adele's party?

.... people   **[2]**

5 Adele is looking at the costs of the food that she bought for the party.

Nibble Platters	**BBQ Buffet**	**Dessert**
£106	£677	£215

(a) She thinks that she has spent less than £985 in total.
Is she correct? Show your working.

Tick (✓) your answer.   ☐ Yes   ☐ No   **[2]**

(b) Write down the most expensive of the costs in words.

....

....   **[1]**

END OF TEST

/ 8

Number: Test 8

There are **5 questions** in this test.
Give yourself **10 minutes** to answer them all.
You **may** use a calculator for this test.

1   What is twenty-seven multiplied by thirty-three?

Tick (✓) your answer.

☐   832

☐   891

☐   918

☐   924   **[1]**

2   Which of these sets of numbers is in order from smallest to largest?

Tick (✓) your answer.

☐   32.3   32.36   32   33

☐   32.3   32   33   32.36

☐   32   32.36   32.3   33

☐   32   32.3   32.36   33   **[1]**

3   What is $\frac{3}{4}$ of 100 km?

.... km   **[1]**

4   Dan has planned the following cycling trip.

Day 1: 278 km
Day 2: 321 km
Day 3: 145 km

Work out an estimate of the total distance by
rounding each daily distance to the nearest 10 km.

.... km   **[2]**

5   Dan has the following vouchers to spend on a new bike.

Voucher £35   Voucher £35   Voucher £35

He buys a bike that costs £449.
He pays using the vouchers and £224 in cash.
He will pay the remaining cost in five equal monthly payments.

How much will he pay each month?

£ ....   **[3]**

END OF TEST

/ 8

Number: Test 9

There are **4 questions** in this test.
Give yourself **10 minutes** to answer them all.
You **may not** use a calculator for this test.

1 What is 340 + 526?

Tick (✓) your answer.

$\square$ 766

$\square$ 866

$\square$ 776

$\square$ 876   **[1]**

2 A sequence starts 4, 10, 16, 22, ...
Which one of these numbers would appear later on in the sequence?

Tick (✓) your answer.

$\square$ 32

$\square$ 33

$\square$ 34

$\square$ 35   **[1]**

3 Use rounding to estimate the answer to 897 − 403.

....   **[1]**

---

4 Charlize runs a delivery company. She has 384 parcels to deliver.

(a) One van can carry at most 36 parcels.

36 parcels

On each delivery trip, a van takes as many parcels as possible and returns after they've all been delivered.

How many trips would it take one van to deliver all of the parcels? How many parcels are delivered on the last trip?

.... trips

The last trip has .... parcels **[3]**

(b) Charlize sends out 12 different vans.
Each of these vans is carrying exactly 32 parcels.

Are all of her parcels out for delivery? Show your working.

Tick (✓) your answer. ☐ Yes ☐ No **[2]**

END OF TEST

/ 8

Number: Test 10

There are **5 questions** in this test.
Give yourself **10 minutes** to answer them all.
You **may** use a calculator for this test.

1   What is 854 ÷ 28?

Tick (✓) your answer.

☐   30 remainder 1

☐   30 remainder 5

☐   30 remainder 14

☐   30 remainder 23   **[1]**

2   What number comes next in the sequence below?

| 1.25 | 1.40 | 1.55 | 1.70 |

Tick (✓) your answer.

☐   1.80

☐   1.85

☐   1.90

☐   1.95   **[1]**

3   What is 753 rounded to the nearest 100?

....   **[1]**

Section One: Number   © CGP — not to be photocopied

4 Tony runs a hotel.
He charges £29 per night, plus an optional £6 for breakfast.

18 guests stayed at the hotel. 5 paid for breakfast.
How much money did Tony earn from these guests?

£ .... **[2]**

5 Tony's hotel had a total of 693 guests last year.
$\frac{2}{3}$ of those guests did **not** pay for breakfast.

(a) Shade the diagram below to show the fraction of
guests who did **not** pay for breakfast last year.

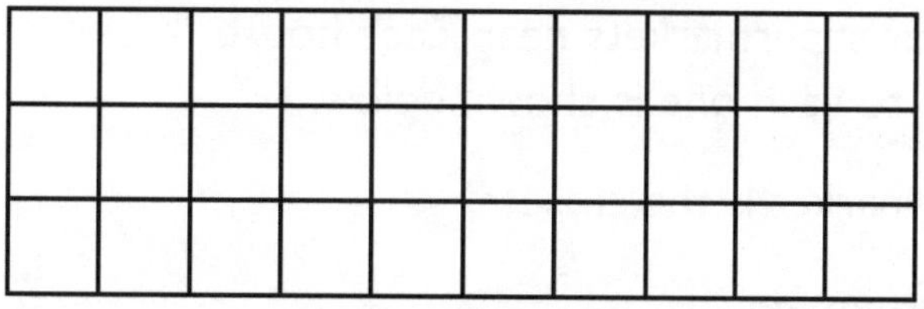

[1]

(b) How many guests **did** pay for breakfast last year?

.... guests **[2]**

END OF TEST

/ 8

Measures, Shape and Space: Test 1

There are **6 questions** in this test.
Give yourself **10 minutes** to answer them all.
You **may** use a calculator for this test.

1 Which of these properties can **never** be true for a rectangle?

Tick (✓) your answer.

☐ It has four sides of the same length.

☐ It has an even number of lines of symmetry.

☐ It has four corners that are right angles.

☐ It has two opposite sides of different lengths. **[1]**

2 There are four supermarkets near Zac's house.
The distance to each one is shown below.

Which supermarket is the closest?

Tick (✓) your answer.

A	B	C	D
2500 m	2.2 km	2.6 km	290 m

☐ ☐ ☐ ☐ **[1]**

3 Look at the map on the right.

In which compass direction is the
supermarket from Zac's house?

.... **[1]**

4 At the supermarket, Zac weighs the four bunches of bananas shown below.
List the weights in order from the lightest to the heaviest.

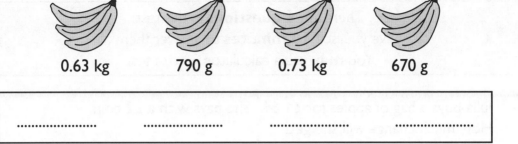

0.63 kg   790 g   0.73 kg   670 g

....   **[1]**

5 Zac has £35 with him.
He spends £28.47.

How much money does he have left to the nearest pound?

£ ....   **[2]**

6 According to his watch, Zac arrived at the supermarket at 2:25 pm.

When he leaves the supermarket that afternoon,
his watch shows the time below.

How long was he in the supermarket for?

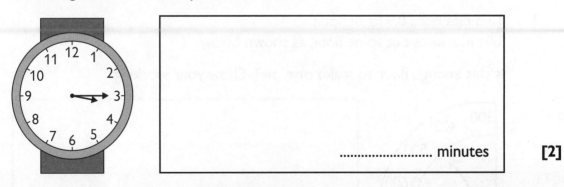

.... minutes   **[2]**

END OF TEST

/ 8

Measures, Shape and Space: Test 2

There are **6 questions** in this test.
Give yourself **10 minutes** to answer them all.
You **may** use a calculator for this test.

1   Julia buys a bag of apples for £1.64. She pays with a £2 coin.
How much change will she get?

Tick (✓) your answer.

☐ 46p   ☐ 44p   ☐ 36p   ☐ 34p   **[1]**

2   Julia is making an apple pie.
The recipe says to use 660 g of apples.

How much is this in kilograms?

.... kg   **[1]**

3   Two pies need 0.9 kg of flour.
Julie measures out some flour, as shown below.

Is this enough flour to make **one** pie? Show your working.

Tick (✓) your answer.   ☐ Yes   ☐ No   **[2]**

---

4 Julia makes the pie and cuts a shape out of pastry
to decorate the top, as shown below.

Draw all of the lines of symmetry on the shape.

[1]

5 She puts the pie in the oven.
The dial on the oven timer is initially set to 0 minutes.

Julia sets the timer to 60 minutes.
What fraction of a circle has she turned the dial?

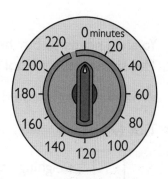

....

[1]

6 Julia takes the pie out of the oven at 17:45.
She needs to let it cool for 1 hour and 40 minutes before serving.

What time can she serve the pie?

....

[2]

END OF TEST

/ 8

Measures, Shape and Space: Test 3

There are **5 questions** in this test.
Give yourself **10 minutes** to answer them all.
You **may** use a calculator for this test.

1 Circle all of the right angles in the 2D shape below.

[1]

2 Yolanda needs to buy her son Raul a new school blazer.
The sizes of the school blazers are based on height.

What instrument could she use to measure Raul's height?

Tick (✓) your answer.

☐ weighing scales   ☐ thermometer

☐ stopwatch   ☐ tape measure   [1]

3 Yolanda wants to catch a bus into town that leaves at 11:05 am.
It will take her 20 minutes to walk from her house to the bus stop.

What is the latest time that Yolanda can set off from her house?

....   [1]

4 Raul is 154 cm tall.

Small
1.4 m - 1.5 m

Medium
1.5 m - 1.6 m

Large
1.6 m - 1.7 m

Which size blazer should Yolanda buy him? Show your working.

.... **[2]**

5 The blazer costs £45.80.
Yolanda pays with three £20 notes.

How much change will she get back?

£ .... **[3]**

END OF TEST

/ 8

Measures, Shape and Space: Test 4

There are **5 questions** in this test.
Give yourself **10 minutes** to answer them all.
You **may not** use a calculator for this test.

1 The sign for a garden centre has been blown over.
What fraction should the sign be turned so it is the correct way up?

Tick (✓) your answer.

☐ quarter turn

☐ half turn

☐ three-quarter turn

☐ full turn   **[1]**

2 What is £10.58 rounded to the nearest 10p?

£ ....   **[1]**

3 This thermometer shows the temperature in the greenhouse.
What is the temperature to the nearest division?

.... °C   **[1]**

---

4 Jinnah is planting a new flower bed.

The seeds need to be at least **65 mm** apart.
Two of the seeds are **6.07 cm** apart.

Are these two seeds far enough apart? Show your working.

Tick (✓) your answer. ☐ Yes ☐ No **[2]**

5 Jinnah has to plant **17** bulbs.
Each bulb needs **92 g** of soil.

There are four bags of soil he can choose from. He wants
to use the **smallest** bag that has enough soil for all his bulbs.

What is the capacity of the bag of soil that he should choose?

Garden Soil 1.25 kg   Garden Soil 1.5 kg   Garden Soil 1.75 kg   Garden Soil 2 kg

.... kg **[3]**

END OF TEST

/ 8

⏱10 Measures, Shape and Space: Test 5

There are **5 questions** in this test.
Give yourself **10 minutes** to answer them all.
You **may not** use a calculator for this test.

1   How long is the line shown below? Give your answer in centimetres.

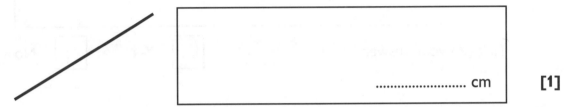

.... cm   **[1]**

2   Brad lives in Bristol. He plans to go on a trip to London.
Which compass direction is London from Bristol?

Tick (✓) your answer.

☐ north

☐ east

☐ south

☐ west

[1]

3   Brad lives 3000 m from the motorway.
The total journey from Brad's house to London is 207 km.

How far does Brad have left to travel once he gets to the motorway?

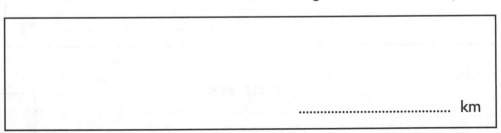

.... km   **[2]**

4   Brad needs $\frac{3}{4}$ of a tank of petrol to drive to London and back.

When Brad arrives in London he has the petrol shown on the scale.
Does he have enough petrol for the return journey?

Tick (✓) your answer.   ☐ Yes   ☐ No   **[1]**

5   On the way to London, Brad stops at a service station to buy lunch.
Part of his receipt is shown below.

Receipt

Sandwich £3.90

Pot of fruit £1.99

Cup of tea £1.05

Total

He pays with a £10 note.
Estimate how much change he receives.

£ ....   **[3]**

END OF TEST

/ 8

Section Two: Measures, Shape and Space

Measures, Shape and Space: Test 6

There are **5 questions** in this test.
Give yourself **10 minutes** to answer them all.
You **may** use a calculator for this test.

1 Which angle in this triangle is the biggest?

Tick (✓) your answer.

    A

    B

    C

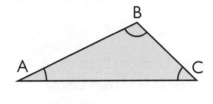

[1]

2 Raiya is lifting weights at the gym. She can safely lift any weight up to **8 kg**. Which of the weights below can she safely lift?

Tick (✓) **all** of your answers.

    850 g

    8.5 kg

    7500 g

    7.5 kg

[1]

3 There are two bottles of water in a vending machine at the gym.
How many millilitres of water are in both bottles combined?

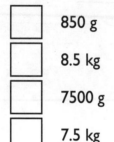

250 ml   0.6 litres

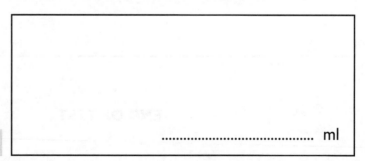

.... ml   [2]

4 The clock shows the time that Raiya gets up for work in the morning.

(a) What time is this on the 24-hour clock?

.... **[1]**

(b) Sometimes Raiya goes for a jog before work.
She gets up 40 minutes earlier on these days.

What time does Raiya get up on days that she goes for a jog?

.... **[1]**

5 Raiya has just bought a new sports shirt and a pair of trainers.

- The sports shirt cost £21.25.
- The trainers **usually** cost £87.30.
- The trainers currently have a discount of £35.50 off.

How much did Raiya pay altogether for the sports shirt and the trainers?

£ .... **[2]**

END OF TEST

/ 8

Section Two: Measures, Shape and Space

Measures, Shape and Space: Test 7

There are **5 questions** in this test.
Give yourself **10 minutes** to answer them all.
You **may** use a calculator for this test.

1 Which triangle below has a right angle?

Tick (✓) your answer.

A   B   C   D

☐   ☐   ☐   ☐   **[1]**

2 Florence and Celia are using the map shown on the right to plan their holiday.

Which direction must they travel in to get from the boat dock to the hotel?

Tick (✓) your answer.

☐ north west   ☐ south west

☐ south east   ☐ north east   **[1]**

3 The total price for the hotel is £362.78.
How much is this rounded to the nearest pound?

£ ....   **[1]**

4 Florence and Celia book a flight and print off the tickets.
Each ticket has a barcode to be scanned at the airport.

(a) Measure the width of the barcode in millimetres.

.... mm **[1]**

(b) The barcode needs to be at least 5 cm wide to be scanned properly.
Is the barcode wide enough? Show your working.

Tick (✓) your answer. ☐ Yes ☐ No **[2]**

5 Florence and Celia's flight departs at 16:55.
They arrive at the airport two and three quarter hours before departure.

What time do they arrive at the airport?
Write your answer in the 12-hour clock.

.... **[2]**

END OF TEST

/ 8

Measures, Shape and Space: Test 8

There are **5 questions** in this test.
Give yourself **10 minutes** to answer them all.
You **may** use a calculator for this test.

1   Which of these measurements is the smallest?

Tick (✓) your answer.

☐   1 litre

☐   0.95 litres

☐   900 ml

☐   1.09 ml   **[1]**

2   Draw all of the lines of symmetry on the shape below.

                                                                                                        [1]

3   Omar works at a restaurant. His shift starts at 1 pm.
The clock on the right shows when his shift ends.

| 2 1 : 0 0 |

How long is his shift?

.... hours   **[1]**

---

4 Omar starts setting a table.
He realises that the tablecloth is too small for the table.

A ruler is placed on the table, as shown below.

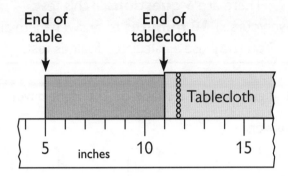

How many inches away from the edge
of the table is the end of the tablecloth?

.... inches   **[2]**

5 On Friday, Omar was given £18.22 in tips.
On Saturday, he was given 96p more in tips than on Friday.

How much tip money did he get in total over Friday and Saturday?

£ ....   **[3]**

END OF TEST

/ 8

Measures, Shape and Space: Test 9

There are **6 questions** in this test.
Give yourself **10 minutes** to answer them all.
You **may** use a calculator for this test.

1   How many right angles does the shape on the right have?

Tick (✓) your answer.

☐ 0   ☐ 1   ☐ 2   ☐ 3   **[1]**

2   Which of these boxes weighs the least?

Tick (✓) your answer.

☐   3 kg   ☐   0.3 kg

☐   300 g   ☐   30 g   **[1]**

3   Jonah is moving house.
The moving van was supposed to arrive at 08:30.

The van turns up later that morning,
at the time shown on the right.

How late is the van?

....   **[1]**

Section Two: Measures, Shape and Space   © CGP — not to be photocopied

4 Jonah hires a lorry for three days to help him move house.

The lorry costs £140.39 a day to hire.
There is also a single booking fee of £15.

How much does the lorry cost to hire in total?

£ ....   **[2]**

5 At the new house, Jonah needs to know the temperature in the kitchen.
What would be an appropriate instrument to use?

....   **[1]**

6 Jonah wants to put a dining table in a room that measures 3 m by 3 m.

The dining table measures 130 cm by 210 cm.
Jonah wants to leave a gap of 50 cm around all sides of the dining table.

Will the dining table fit? Show your working.

Tick (✓) your answer.   ☐ Yes   ☐ No   **[2]**

END OF TEST

/ 8

Section Two: Measures, Shape and Space

Measures, Shape and Space: Test 10

There are **5 questions** in this test.
Give yourself **10 minutes** to answer them all.
You **may** use a calculator for this test.

1 Which shape below has more than two lines of symmetry?

Tick (✓) your answer.

☐   ☐   ☐   ☐   **[1]**

2 Elliot needs to post an application form.
It has a width of 25 cm and cannot be folded.

He chooses the smallest envelope into which it will fit.
Which envelope does he choose?

Tick (✓) your answer.

248 mm   242 mm   259 mm   252 mm

☐   ☐   ☐   ☐   **[1]**

3 First class postage costs £1.06 and second class postage costs 83p.
How much more does first class postage cost than second class postage?

....   **[1]**

4 Elliot is going to an interview in the afternoon.

(a) The interview starts at 13:20
and will last 30 minutes.

Draw hands on this clock to show
the time that the interview finishes.

[1]

(b) It will take Elliot 35 minutes to walk to the interview from his house.
He wants to arrive at least 15 minutes before it starts.

What is the latest time he should set off?

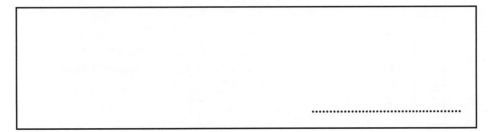

.... **[2]**

5 Elliot feels thirsty whilst waiting for his interview.
He drinks 0.2 litres of water from his bottle.

The remaining water in his bottle is shown on the right.

How many millilitres of water did he start with?

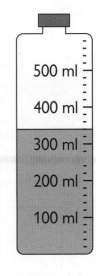

.... ml **[2]**

END OF TEST

/ 8

Section Two: Measures, Shape and Space

Handling Data: Test 1

There are **4 questions** in this test.
Give yourself **10 minutes** to answer them all.
You **may** use a calculator for this test.

1   A gift list for a wedding is shown below. Aaron wants to buy an item
that costs between £25 and £50. How many of the items could he buy?

Tick (✓) your answer.

☐ 4

☐ 5

☐ 6

☐ 7

Gift List
saucepan (£34), microwave (£65), vacuum cleaner (£249), iron (£54), casserole dish (£19), blender (£23), toaster (£30), stockpot (£26), wok (£32), coffee maker (£149), knife set (£48), kettle (£27)

[1]

2   Chandana's wedding day is circled on the calendar below.

February						
Mo	**Tu**	**We**	**Th**	**Fr**	**Sa**	**Su**
27	28	29	30	31	1	2
3	4	5	6	7	8	9
10	11	12	13	14	15	16
17	18	19	20	21	22	23
24	25	26	27	28	29	1

(a)   If today is January 27th, how many weekends
are there left until the wedding day?

.... weekends   **[1]**

(b)   Aaron needs to take his suit for dry cleaning.
He can go on a Tuesday or a Thursday, but not before the 15th.

Circle the first possible date that he can go on the calendar above.   **[1]**

3 Chandana is making a bar chart to show some of the wedding costs.

- The dress costs £150 more than the photographer.
- The photographer costs £75 less than the flowers.

Add the cost of the photographer and the flowers to the bar chart below.

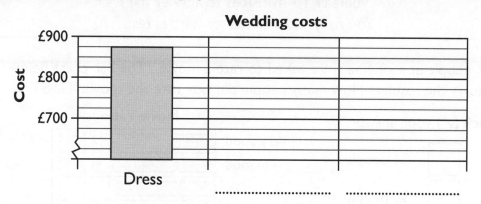

Wedding costs

[2]

4 This graph shows the number of weddings held at a venue over six months.

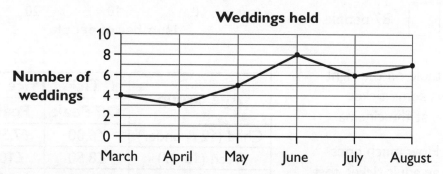

Weddings held

Chandana says, "The month with the most weddings had exactly twice as many weddings as the month with the fewest."

Is she correct? Show your working to justify your answer.

Tick (✓) your answer. ☐ Yes ☐ No   [3]

END OF TEST

/ 8

Handling Data: Test 2

There are **4 questions** in this test.
Give yourself **10 minutes** to answer them all.
You **may** use a calculator for this test.

1 51 people at a cinema were asked to rate a movie. The bar chart below shows the results. How many people did **not** rate the movie 'Good'?

Tick (✓) your answer.

☐ 34 people

☐ 35 people

☐ 36 people

☐ 37 people

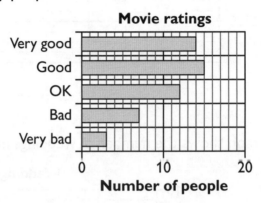

[1]

2 The table on the right shows some ticket prices at the cinema.

Age Group	Ticket Price	
	Off-Peak	**Peak**
Child (12 & under)	£6.00	£7.50
Teen (13-17)	£8.50	£10
Adult (18+)	£9.75	£11.25

(a) How much does an adult ticket cost during off-peak hours?

£ .... [1]

(b) How many peak time teen tickets could you buy with £45?

.... tickets [1]

---

3 Davina and her three friends are planning to see a movie.
The showtimes and number of seats available are shown in this table.

	12:00	13:00	14:40	15:40	17:20	18:20
Fri	5	14	32	35*	12*	8
Sat	26*	Sold out	Sold out	Sold out	37*	Sold out
Sun	3	Sold out	14	20*	15*	Sold out

*3D only

They can go any time during the weekend or after 17:00 on weekdays.
They do not want to see it in 3D.

Write down all of the showings that they are willing and able to see.

....

.... **[2]**

4 The table below shows the amount of popcorn sold at the cinema.

Day	Thu	Fri	Sat	Sun
Amount (pounds, lb)	120	180	160	100

Draw and label a line graph on the grid below to show this information.

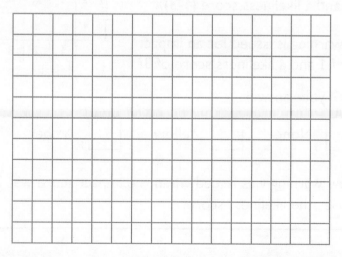

[3]

END OF TEST

/ 8

Handling Data: Test 3

There are **3 questions** in this test.
Give yourself **10 minutes** to answer them all.
You **may** use a calculator for this test.

1   This map shows some temperatures in °C.
Which of these lists is in order from the lowest to highest temperature?

Tick (✓) your answer.

- [ ]   Aberdeen, Belfast, Hull

- [ ]   Hull, Belfast, Plymouth

- [ ]   Newcastle, Plymouth, Hull

- [ ]   Hull, Edinburgh, Liverpool

[1]

Aberdeen **2**
Edinburgh **4**
Belfast **6**
Newcastle **0**
Liverpool **6**
Hull **3**
Cardiff **6**
London **8**
Plymouth **4**

2   Using the diagram on the right, a weather office issues warnings based on an impact score (1-3) and a likeliness score (1-3).

Impact			
3	A	A	R
2	Y	A	A
1		Y	Y
	1	2	3

-Likeliness➤

Key:
- [ ] None
- Y Yellow
- A Amber
- R Red

(a)   What warning is issued for an impact score of 1 and a likeliness score of 3?

Tick (✓) your answer.

- [ ] None   - [ ] Yellow   - [ ] Amber   - [ ] Red   **[1]**

(b)   A yellow warning was issued when the impact score was 2.
What was the likeliness score?

....   **[1]**

---

3 One year, Sam records the weather warnings issued each day in his area.
The results for December are shown in the table below.

(a) Complete the table.

Type	Tally	Frequency
No warning	ⵜⵜⵜ ⵜⵜⵜ ⵜⵜⵜ II	....
Yellow	....	8
Amber	....	4
Red	II	....

[2]

(b) This line graph shows the total number of warnings each month.
Complete the graph by adding the data for December from part **(a)**.

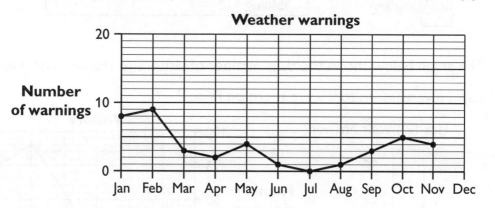

[1]

(c) Sam says that a month had extreme weather if
the number of warnings that month was more than 5.

Write down all the months that Sam would say had extreme weather.

....

....

[2]

END OF TEST

/ 8

Handling Data: Test 4

There are **4 questions** in this test.
Give yourself **10 minutes** to answer them all.
You **may** use a calculator for this test.

1   The table below shows the cost of activities at a lake.
How much does it cost altogether for a group of four to go sailing?

Tick (✓) your answer.

☐ £75

☐ £100

☐ £300

☐ £400

Activity	Number of people	Cost per person
Rafting	1-8	£60
Sailing	1-2	£100
	3-4	£75
Water Skiing	1-6	£80

[1]

2   The graph below shows the daily number of visitors to the lake last week.

(a) How many visitors were there on Friday?

Tick (✓) your answer.

☐ 50

☐ 51

☐ 55

☐ 60

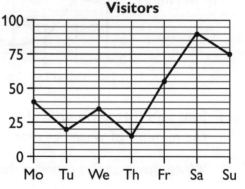

[1]

(b) On how many days were there fewer than 40 visitors?

.... days   [1]

---

3 Laura wants to go rafting with her friends. The box on the right shows the dates when each person is available this month.

Laura: 7ᵗʰ 9ᵗʰ 13ᵗʰ 17ᵗʰ
Sid: 2ⁿᵈ 5ᵗʰ 13ᵗʰ 17ᵗʰ
Cara: 4ᵗʰ 5ᵗʰ 12ᵗʰ 13ᵗʰ

(a) On which date can the group go rafting?

.... **[1]**

(b) What is the earliest date that Sid and Cara could go without Laura?

.... **[1]**

4 Laura has recorded the different types of fish she has seen in the lake.

Type of fish	Chub	Pike	Trout
Number seen	70	10	30

Draw and label a bar chart to show this information on the grid below.

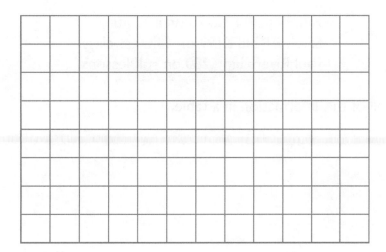

[3]

END OF TEST

/ 8

Handling Data: Test 5

1   This bar chart shows the bids made by two people at an auction.
How much more did Beth bid on the chair than Terry?

Tick (✓) your answer.

☐ £10

☐ £15

☐ £20

☐ £25

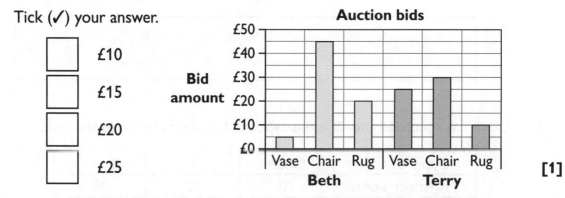

[1]

2   This list shows the most expensive bids made at the auction.

> Kim Ji-hun bid £275 on a painting.
> Sarah Ali bid £199 on a fitness class.
> Paul Rivers bid £280 on golf lessons.

Organise all of this information in a table.

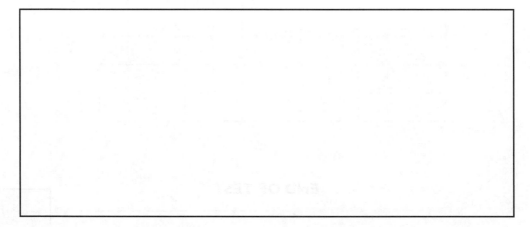

[2]

3 Mo has made a table to show information on the bids made at the auction.

Bid amount	Number of bids made	Number of items sold
Less than £50	50	7
£50 to £100	75	12
More than £100	....	3
Totals:	185	22

(a) Complete the table. **[1]**

(b) How many bids worth £50 or more were made?

.... bids **[1]**

(c) Mo will donate £17 for every item that sold for £100 or less.

He thinks that he will donate more than £300.
Is he correct? Show your working.

Tick (✓) your answer. ☐ Yes ☐ No **[3]**

END OF TEST

/ 8

Mixed Practice: Test 1

There are **5 questions** in this test.
Give yourself **10 minutes** to answer them all.
You **may not** use a calculator for this test.

1 Jake wakes up in the morning. His clock is shown below. What time is it?

Tick (✓) your answer.

☐ 9:20 am

☐ 9:20 pm

☐ 9:40 am

☐ 10:20 am

[1]

2 Jake has to drive to all the clients in the table below today.
He wants to visit the nearest client first. Who should he visit first?

Tick (✓) your answer.

☐ A. Smith

☐ C. G. Peters

☐ F. Miller

☐ D. Bashir

Name	Distance
A. Smith	1.4 km
C. G. Peters	990 m
F. Miller	0.98 km
D. Bashir	2.3 km

[1]

3 Jake drove a total of 308 km last week.
How far is this to the nearest 10 km?

.... km   **[1]**

© CGP — not to be photocopied

4 Jake charges his clients £34 per hour.
How much does he charge for 17 hours?

£ .... **[2]**

5 This graph shows how much Jake has earned in the last six weeks.

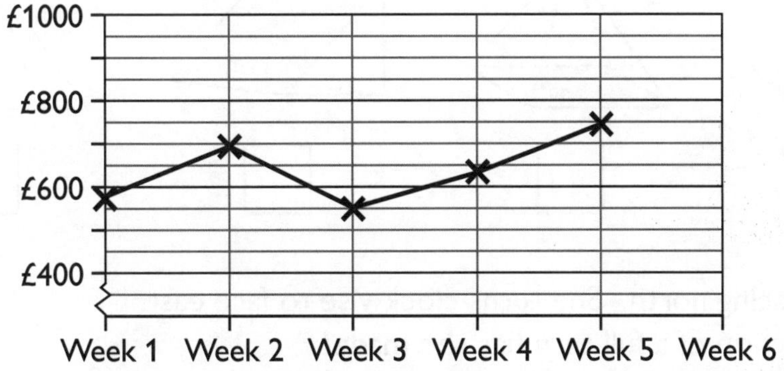

(a) Jake earned £700 in Week 6. Use this data to complete the graph. **[1]**

(b) In which week did Jake earn the least?

Week .... **[1]**

(c) In how many of the weeks did Jake earn more than £650?

.... weeks **[1]**

END OF TEST

/ 8

Section Four: Mixed Practice

Mixed Practice: Test 2

There are **5 questions** in this test.
Give yourself **10 minutes** to answer them all.
You **may** use a calculator for this test.

1 Look at the shaded faces of these 3D shapes.
Which one does not have at least one right angle?

Tick (✓) your answer.

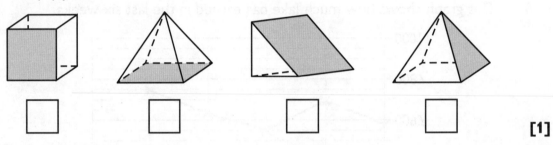

☐   ☐   ☐   ☐   **[1]**

2 Maria is facing north. She turns clockwise to face east.
What fraction of a full turn has she made?

Tick (✓) your answer.

☐ $\frac{1}{2}$

☐ $\frac{1}{3}$

☐ $\frac{1}{4}$

☐ $\frac{3}{4}$ **[1]**

3 Maria catches a bus. Her ticket is shown on the right.
She pays with £5. How much change did she get?

£ ....

Bus Ticket
Adult Single
£2.65
Dean St.
to
Applegate

[1]

4   At a travel shop, Maria buys a bus pass for £762.
She will pay for it in 12 equal monthly payments.

How much will she pay each month?

.... [2]

5   A bus timetable is shown below.

Applegate	13:00	13:15	13:30†	13:45
King Square	13:06	13:21	13:36†	13:51
Riverside	13:14	13:29	13:44†	13:59
Dean Street	13:21	13:36	13:51†	14:06

†no wheelchair ramp

(a)   How long does a bus from Applegate to Dean Street take?

.... minutes [1]

Maria is at Applegate bus stop.
She wants to get to Dean Street by 14:00.
She needs a bus that has a wheelchair ramp.

(b)   At what time will the latest bus that she could catch leave Applegate?

.... [2]

END OF TEST

/ 8

Mixed Practice: Test 3

1   Which is the most suitable instrument to measure 5 ml of cough syrup?

Tick (✓) your answer.

☐   a ruler

☐   a teaspoon

☐   a protractor

☐   a thermometer   **[1]**

2   A pharmacy sells cards. Each card costs £2.25.
How much is this to the nearest 10p?

Tick (✓) your answer.

☐   £2.00

☐   £2.30

☐   £2.20

☐   £2.10   **[1]**

3   Aamir measures the width of a card.
What is the width of this card?

```
.........................................
```
[1]

4   The pharmacy has a display of reading glasses.

(a) The box below contains the strengths of 15 glasses.
Use this data to complete the frequency table.

2.00	1.50	3.00
3.00	3.00	2.50
3.00	1.50	1.50
2.50	3.00	2.50
1.50	2.00	3.00

Strength	Frequency
1.50	
2.00	
2.50	
3.00	

[1]

(b) $\frac{3}{10}$ of the glasses have black frames.
What fraction of the glasses do **not** have black frames?

$$\frac{\boxed{}}{\boxed{}}$$

[1]

5   Dental floss is sold in strings that are 47 m long.
Aamir thinks that 21 of these strings cover a distance of 1 km.

Is he correct? Show your working.

Tick (✓) your answer. ☐ Yes ☐ No   [3]

END OF TEST

/ 8

Section Four: Mixed Practice

Mixed Practice: Test 4

There are **5 questions** in this test.
Give yourself **10 minutes** to answer them all.
You **may** use a calculator for this test.

1   What is £352.20 in words?

Tick (✓) your answer.

☐   thirty-five pounds and twenty-two pence

☐   three hundred and fifty-two pounds and two pence

☐   three hundred and fifty pounds and twenty-two pence

☐   three hundred and fifty-two pounds and twenty pence   **[1]**

2   Which of these shapes have more than two lines of symmetry?

Tick (✓) **all** of your answers.

☐   ☐   ☐   ☐   **[1]**

3   Anya is mixing a yoghurt drink.
She pours 260 ml of yoghurt into an empty jug.

How many **litres** of yoghurt are in the jug?

.... litres   **[1]**

---

4   Anya weighs out 150 g of fruit. Blueberries make up $\frac{1}{5}$ of the fruit.
What is the mass of these blueberries?

.... g   **[2]**

5   Anya is looking for bottles in which to sell her drink.
She finds some available with the following capacities.

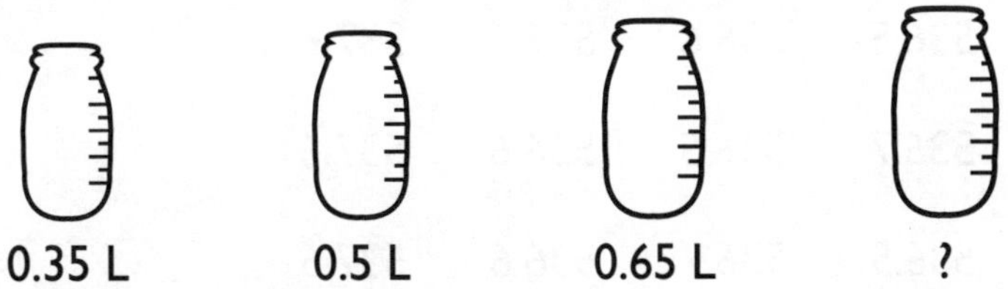

0.35 L   0.5 L   0.65 L   ?

(a) The capacities follow a pattern.
What is the capacity of the largest bottle?

.... L   **[1]**

(b) A partially-filled 0.5 L bottle is shown below. How much more
drink can be poured into the bottle before it reaches its capacity?

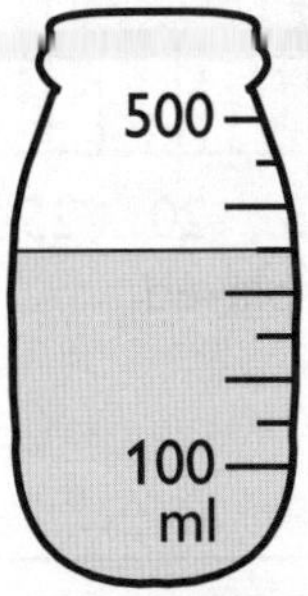

500

100
ml

.... ml   **[2]**

END OF TEST

/ 8

Mixed Practice: Test 5

There are **4 questions** in this test.
Give yourself **10 minutes** to answer them all.
You **may** use a calculator for this test.

1   Which of these sets of numbers is in order from smallest to largest?

Tick (✓) your answer.

	536.7	537.6	536.5	536.6
	536.5	536.6	536.7	537.6
	536.7	536.5	536.6	537.6
	536.5	536.7	536.6	537.6

[1]

2   This bar chart shows the games played by a football team in one season.
How many games were played at the weekend?

Tick (✓) your answer.

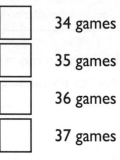 34 games

 35 games

 36 games

 37 games

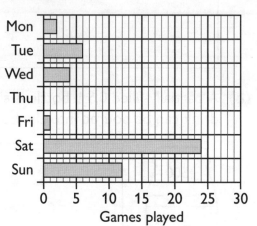

[1]

3   Work out 360 ÷ 16. Give your answer with a remainder.

.... remainder ....   [1]

---

4 A football scout has collected data on four players.

Player 1		**Player 2**	
Games played:	562	Games played:	652
Cost (£ millions):	6.95	Cost (£ millions):	7.95

Player 3		**Player 4**	
Games played:	698	Games played:	599
Cost (£ millions):	7.39	Cost (£ millions):	6.89

(a) Organise all of this information in a table.

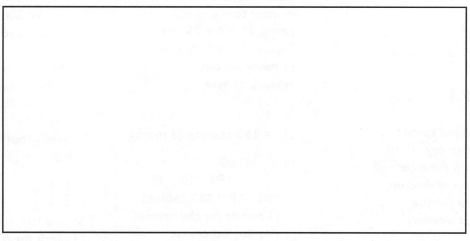

[2]

(b) How much does the most expensive player cost?

£ .... million [1]

(c) Work out the difference between the number of games played by the players who have played the most and fewest games.

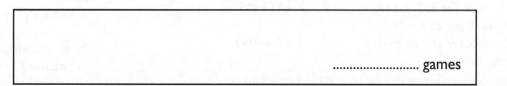

.... games [2]

END OF TEST

/ 8

Answers

Section One: Number

Test 1 — pages 2 and 3

1   **386** *(1 mark)*

2   $\frac{1}{2}$ *(1 mark)*

You can divide the top and bottom of $\frac{5}{10}$ by 5.

3
$$\begin{array}{r} 3\ 2 \\ \times\quad 7 \\ \hline 2\ 2\ 4 \\ \scriptstyle 1 \end{array}$$ *(1 mark)*

4
$$6\,\overline{)3\,^3 7\,^1 2}^{\ 0\ 6\ 2}$$

So she will spend **£62** each day.
(1 mark for a correct method of division, 1 mark for the correct answer)

5
$$\begin{array}{r} 3\ 3\ 9 \\ +\ 5\ 1\ 4 \\ \hline 8\ 5\ 3 \\ \scriptstyle 1 \end{array}$$

So the total distance is 853 miles.
853 miles − 100 miles = 753 miles, so she has 753 miles to go.
This is more than 749 miles.
No — she is incorrect.
(1 mark for 339 + 514, 1 mark for 853 – 100, 1 mark for the correct conclusion)

Test 2 — pages 4 and 5

1   **nine hundred and fifty-six** *(1 mark)*

2   **4.21   4.12   2.41** *(1 mark)*

3   **430 employees** *(1 mark)*

4   Add 4 to get from one number to the next.
Large: 21 + 4 = **25 cm**
Super: 25 + 4 = **29 cm**
(1 mark for each correct answer)

5   a) 24 × 15
     = **360 tablets** *(1 mark)*

   b) $\frac{1}{10}$ of 180
        = 180 ÷ 10 = 18
   180 − 18 = **162 tablets**
   (2 marks for the correct answer, otherwise 1 mark for a correct method)

Test 3 — pages 6 and 7

1
$$\begin{array}{r} 1\ 3 \\ \times\quad 5 \\ \hline 6\ 5 \\ \scriptstyle 1 \end{array}$$ *(1 mark)*

2   **5.36** *(1 mark)*

3   $\frac{3}{5}$ *(1 mark)*

Test 4 — pages 8 and 9

4   a)
$$\begin{array}{r} ^2\cancel{3}\ ^{15}\cancel{5}\ 9 \\ -\quad 6\ 1 \\ \hline 2\ 9\ 8 \end{array}\ \text{minutes}$$
(1 mark for a correct method of subtraction, 1 mark for the correct answer)

b) E.g. 359 − 61
        ≈ 360 − 60
        = 300 minutes
        ≈ 298 minutes ✔
                    (1 mark)
There are other correct ways of checking your answer. For example, you could round 298 to 300 and 61 to 60, then do 300 + 60 = 360 ≈ 359 ✓

5
$$4\,\overline{)3\,^3 9\,^3 2}^{\ 0\ 9\ 8}$$
So one tyre costs **£98**.
(1 mark for a correct method of division, 1 mark for the correct answer)

Test 4 — pages 8 and 9

1   **980** *(1 mark)*

2   660 kg ÷ 5
     = **132 kg** *(1 mark)*

3   **Three hundred and seventeen** *(1 mark)*

4 a) 8 × 9 = 72 seats
72 × £13 = **£936**
*(2 marks for the correct
answer, otherwise
1 mark for multiplying
two of the numbers
together)*

b) 845 ÷ 13 = 65 tickets sold
72 − 65 = **7 tickets** unsold
*(2 marks for the correct
answer, otherwise
1 mark for a correct
method)*
You could also do:
£936 − £845 = £91
£91 ÷ £13 = 7 tickets unsold

5 Add 14 to get from one
number to the next.
The fifth seat number
is 47 + 14 = 61.
No — Valerie will not be
asked to give feedback.
*(1 mark for the correct
conclusion with working
shown)*

Test 5 — pages 10 and 11

1 $\frac{9}{16}$ *(1 mark)*

2
```
  1 9 0
  1 6 0
+ 1 1 5
  4 6 5
    1
```
So the total cost
is **£465**. *(1 mark)*

3 The cheapest painting
costs £314, which rounds
to **£310**. *(1 mark)*

4 a) **2.00 m** *(1 mark)*

b)
```
      2 8
  ×   1 4
  1 1 ₃2
+ 2 8 0
  3 9 2  hooks
```
*(1 mark for a
correct method of
multiplication,
1 mark for the
correct answer)*

c) Add 0.08 to get from one
number to the next.
2.16 + 0.08 = **2.24 m**
2.24 + 0.08 = **2.32 m**
*(1 mark for each
correct answer)*

Test 6 — pages 12 and 13

1 412 − 179 = **233** *(1 mark)*

2 **600** *(1 mark)*

3 624 ÷ 53 = <u>11</u>.773...
<u>11</u> × 53 = 583 and then
remainder = 624 − 583 = 41
11 remainder 41 *(1 mark)*

4 256 − 231 = 25, so there is a
special issue every 25 issues.
This means there are **24
ordinary issues** between
each pair of special issues.
(1 mark)

5 a) 24 × £5 = **£120** *(1 mark)*

b) Offer A:
$\frac{1}{4}$ of £120
= £120 ÷ 4 = £30
Offer B:
5 × £5 = £25
£30 is more than £25,
so **Offer A** saves Micah
more money.
*(1 mark for a correct
calculation for Offer A,
1 mark for a correct
calculation for Offer B,
1 mark for the correct
conclusion with working)*
There are other ways you
could answer this question
— and you'd still get the
marks. For example, you
could work out how much
Micah would spend after
using each of the offers, or
you could work out how
many magazines he would
effectively have to pay for.

Test 7 — pages 14 and 15

1 **164.79** *(1 mark)*

2 **20.5** *(1 mark)*

3 21 × 39 ≈ 20 × 40
= **800** *(1 mark)*

4 3 × 10 = 30 people invited
30 − 3 = **27 people**
*(1 mark for a correct
method, 1 mark for the
correct answer)*

5 a)
```
    1 0 6
    6 7 7
  + 2 1 5
    9 9 8
        1
```
£998 is more than £985.
No — Adele is incorrect.
*(1 mark for £998,
1 mark for the
correct conclusion)*

b) **Six hundred and
seventy-seven pounds**
(1 mark)

Test 8 — pages 16 and 17

1 **27 × 33 = 891** *(1 mark)*

2 **32 32.3 32.36 33**
(1 mark)

3 **75 km** *(1 mark)*

4 278 + 321 + 145
≈ 280 + 320 + 150
= **750 km**
*(2 marks for the correct
answer, otherwise 1 mark
for correctly rounding
each distance)*

5 £449 − 3 × £35 − £224
= £449 − £105 − £224
= £120
£120 ÷ 5 = **£24**
*(3 marks for the correct
answer, otherwise
2 marks for £120 or
1 mark for 3 × £35)*

Test 9 — pages 18 and 19

1
```
    3 4 0
  + 5 2 6
    8 6 6
```
(1 mark)

2 Add 6 to get from one
number to the next.
22 + 6 = 28 and then
28 + 6 = **34**. *(1 mark)*

3 897 − 403 ≈ 900 − 400
= **500** *(1 mark)*

4 a)
```
        0 1 0 remainder 24
  3 6 │3³8²4
```
So it would take **11 trips**.
The last trip has
24 parcels.
*(1 mark for calculating
384 ÷ 36, 1 mark for
11 trips, 1 mark for
24 parcels)*
10 trips × 36 parcels
= 360 parcels, so this
isn't enough trips.
11 × 36 = 396, which is
enough trips.

b)
```
      3 2
  ×   1 2
      6 4
  + 3 2 0
    3 8 4
```
Yes — all the parcels
are out for delivery.
*(1 mark for 32 × 12,
1 mark for the
correct conclusion)*

Test 10 — pages 20 and 21

1 **30 remainder 14** *(1 mark)*

2 **1.85** *(1 mark)*

3 **800** *(1 mark)*

4 18 × £29 = £522
5 × £6 = £30
£522 + £30 = **£552**
*(2 marks for the correct
answer, otherwise
1 mark for calculating
either £522 or £30)*

5 a) E.g.

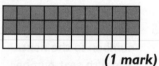

(1 mark)

Shading any 20 squares on
the grid would get you the
mark.

b) $\frac{1}{3}$ of 693
= 693 ÷ 3 = **231 guests**
*(1 mark for a correct
method to find one
third of 693,
1 mark for the
correct answer)*

Section 2: Measures, Shape and Space

Test 1 — pages 22 and 23

1   **It has two opposite sides of different lengths.** *(1 mark)*

2   **D** *(1 mark)*

3   **south west** *(1 mark)*

4   **0.63 kg, 670 g, 0.73 kg, 790 g** *(1 mark)*

5   £35 − £28.47 = £6.53. £6.53 is **£7** when rounded to the nearest pound. *(1 mark for £6.53, 1 mark for rounding correctly)*

6   The watch shows 3:15 pm. 2:25 pm → 3:15 pm = **50 minutes** *(2 marks for the correct answer, otherwise 1 mark for reading 3:15)*

Test 2 — pages 24 and 25

1   **36p** *(1 mark)*

2   **0.66 kg** *(1 mark)*

3   0.9 kg = 900 g So one pie needs 900 ÷ 2 = 450 g of flour. The arrow on the scale is just past the 450 g mark. **Yes** — this is enough.

(1 mark for evidence of reading the scale correctly or converting units, 1 mark for the correct conclusion with working)

4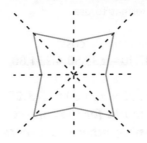

(1 mark for all lines correct)

5   $\frac{1}{4}$ *(1 mark)*

6   After 1 hour it will be 18:45. After 1 hour, the pie needs another 40 minutes to cool. 40 minutes after 18:45 is **19:25 or 7:25 pm.** *(2 marks for a correct answer, otherwise 1 mark for 19:25 pm or 07:25 or some correct working)*

Test 3 — pages 26 and 27

1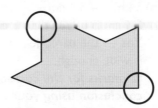

(1 mark for both right angles)

2   **tape measure** *(1 mark)*

3   **10:45 am** *(1 mark)*

4   154 cm = 1.54 m 1.54 m is between 1.5 m and 1.6 m, so she should buy the **medium**. *(1 mark for a correct conversion, 1 mark for choosing the correct size)*

5   3 × £20 = £60 £60 − £45.80 = **£14.20** *(1 mark for £60, 1 mark for a correct method, 1 mark for £14.20 in the correct money format)*

Test 4 — pages 28 and 29

1   **half turn** *(1 mark)*

2   **£10.60** *(1 mark)*

3   **26 °C** *(1 mark)*

4   6.07 cm = 60.7 mm 60.7 mm is less than 65 mm. **No** — the two seeds are not far enough apart. *(1 mark for converting units, 1 mark for the correct conclusion with working)*

5
```
      9 2
  ×   1 7
  6 4₁4
+ 9 2 0
  1 5 6 4  g
```
1564 g = 1.564 kg, so he needs the **1.75 kg** bag of soil. *(1 mark for a correct method of multiplication, 1 mark for 1564 g, 1 mark for the correct answer with working)*

Test 5 — pages 30 and 31

1   **4.5 cm (1 mark)**
Answers between 4.4 cm and
4.6 cm would get the mark.

2   **east (1 mark)**

3   3000 m = 3 km
207 km – 3 km = **204 km**
**(1 mark for using 3 km,
1 mark for the correct
answer)**

4   The dial is only slightly below
$\frac{3}{4}$ of a tank. He needs $\frac{3}{4}$ to
get there and back, so only
half as much to get back.
Yes — he does have
enough petrol. **(1 mark)**

5   Sandwich ≈ £4
Pot of fruit ≈ £2
Cup of tea ≈ £1
£4 + £2 + £1 = £7
£10 – £7 = **£3**
**(1 mark for estimating
correctly, 1 mark for £7,
1 mark for the correct
answer)**

Test 6 — pages 32 and 33

1   **B (1 mark)**

2   **850 g, 7500 g** and **7.5 kg**
(1 mark for all three)

3   0.6 litres = 600 ml
250 ml + 600 ml = **850 ml**
**(2 marks for the correct
answer, otherwise 1 mark
for converting units)**

4   a) **07:20 (1 mark)**

   b) **06:40 (1 mark)**
You could also get the mark
by writing 6:40 am here
since you're not told which
format to use.

5   The trainers cost
£87.30 – £35.50 = £51.80.
So Raiya paid a total of
£21.25 + £51.80 = **£73.05.**
**(2 marks for the correct
answer, otherwise 1 mark
for a correct method)**
You could alternatively apply
the discount to the total cost:
£21.25 + £87.30 = £108.55
£108.55 – £32.50 = £73.05

Test 7 — pages 34 and 35

1   **C (1 mark)**

2   **north east (1 mark)**

3   **£363 (1 mark)**

4   a) **54 mm (1 mark)**
Answers between 53 mm and
55 mm would get the mark.

   b) 54 mm = 5.4 cm
5.4 cm is bigger than 5 cm.
Yes — the barcode
is wide enough.
**(2 marks for the correct
conclusion using your
answer from part (a)
with working shown,
otherwise 1 mark for
converting your answer
from part (a) correctly)**

5   2 hours before 16:55 is
14:55. Three quarters of an
hour before 14:55 is 14:10.
14:10 is **2:10 pm** in the
12-hour clock.
**(2 marks for the correct
answer, otherwise 1 mark
for 14:10)**

Test 8 — pages 36 and 37

1   **1.09 ml (1 mark)**

2

**(1 mark for both lines
correct and no extra lines)**

3   1 pm is 13:00 on the 24-hour
clock. 21 – 13 = **8 hours.**
(1 mark)

4   11 – 5 = **6 inches**
**(2 marks for the correct
answer, otherwise 1 mark
for evidence of reading the
ruler correctly)**

5   96p = £0.96
£18.22 + £0.96 = £19.18,
so on Saturday he got
£19.18 in tips.
£18.22 + £19.18 = £37.40, so
he got **£37.40** in tips in total.
**(1 mark for £19.18, 1 mark
for adding the amounts,
1 mark for £37.40 in
correct money format)**

Alternatively, you could do:
2 × £18.22 = £36.44
£36.44 + £0.96 = £37.40

Test 9 — pages 38 and 39

1 **2** *(1 mark)*

2 **30 g** *(1 mark)*

3 It's in the morning, so the time on the clock is 09:40, so the van is **1 hour and 10 minutes** or **70 minutes** late. *(1 mark)*

4 £140.39 × 3 = £421.17.
Cost = £421.17 + £15
= **£436.17**
(2 marks for the correct answer, otherwise 1 mark for £421.17)

5 **thermometer** *(1 mark)*

6 He needs 50 cm on each side of the dining table, so add 50 cm × 2 = 100 cm to the length and width of the dining table.
130 cm + 100 cm = 230 cm
210 cm + 100 cm = 310 cm
230 cm = 2.3 m
(less than 3 m)
310 cm = 3.1 m
(more than 3 m)
No — the dining table will not fit.
(1 mark for finding the size of the space needed, 1 mark for the correct conclusion)
You could alternatively subtract 50 cm from 3 m to find the largest size that the length and width of the table could be.

Test 10 — pages 40 and 41

1 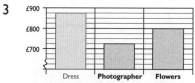 *(1 mark)*

2 25 cm = 250 mm
He chooses the envelope with width **252 mm**.
(1 mark)

3 £1.06 = 106p
106p − 83p
= **23p** or **£0.23** *(1 mark)*

4 a)

(1 mark)

b) 35 + 15 = 50, so he needs to leave 50 minutes before 13:20.
13:20 − 50 mins = **12:30**
(2 marks for the correct answer, otherwise 1 mark for a correct method)
You could also do:
13:20 − 35 mins = 12:45
12:45 − 15 mins = 12:30

5 0.2 litres = 200 ml
There is 340 ml of water left in the bottle.
200 + 340 = **540 ml**
(2 marks for the correct answer, otherwise 1 mark for reading the scale correctly)

Section Three: Handling Data

Test 1 — pages 42 and 43

1 **6** *(1 mark)*

2 a) **4 weekends** *(1 mark)*

b)

	February					
Mo	Tu	We	Th	Fr	Sa	Su
27	28	29	30	31	1	2
3	4	5	6	7	8	9
10	11	12	13	14	15	16
17	18	19	20	21	22	23
24	25	26	27	28	29	1

(1 mark)

3 *(1 mark for a bar labelled 'photographer' at £725, 1 mark for a bar labelled 'flowers' at £800)*
It doesn't matter in which order you've drawn the bars.

4 Most weddings: 8 (in June)
Fewest weddings: 3 (in April)
But twice 3 is 2 × 3 = 6, not 8.
No — Chandana is wrong.
(1 mark for reading at least one correct value off the graph, 1 mark for using both values correctly, 1 mark for the correct conclusion with working)

Test 2 — pages 44 and 45

1 51 − 15 = **36 people**
(1 mark)

2 a) **£9.75** *(1 mark)*

b) 45 ÷ 10 = 4.5
So **4 tickets** can
be bought. *(1 mark)*

3 **Friday at 18:20** and
Sunday at 14:40
*(1 mark for each correct
showing, lose a mark for
each incorrect showing)*

4 E.g.

*(1 mark for four points
joined and labels to show
the four days, 1 mark for
a correct scale, 1 mark for
all points plotted at the
correct heights)*

Test 3 — pages 46 and 47

1 **Hull, Edinburgh,
Liverpool** *(1 mark)*

2 a) **Yellow** *(1 mark)*

b) **1** *(1 mark)*

3 a)

Type	Tally	Freq.
No warning	ЖЖ ЖЖ ЖЖ II	17
Yellow	ЖЖ III	8
Amber	IIII	4
Red	II	2

*(1 mark for a correct
tally column, 1 mark
for a correct frequency
column)*

b)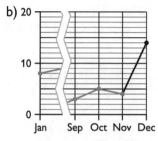

(1 mark)

c) **January, February** and
December
*(2 marks for three
correct with none
incorrect, otherwise
1 mark for at least
one correct with
none incorrect)*

Test 4 — pages 48 and 49

1 4 × £75 = **£300** *(1 mark)*

2 a) **55** *(1 mark)*

b) **3 days** *(1 mark)*

3 a) **13th** *(1 mark)*

b) **5th** *(1 mark)*

4 E.g.

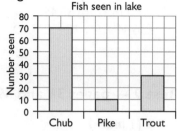

*(1 mark for three bars
drawn with correct labels,
1 mark for a correct scale,
1 mark for bars drawn to
the correct heights)*

Test 5 — pages 50 and 51

1 £45 − £30 = **£15** *(1 mark)*

2 E.g.

Name	Bid	Item
Kim Ji-hun	£275	Painting
Sarah Ali	£199	Fitness class
Paul Rivers	£280	Golf lessons

*(1 mark for a suitable table
format, 1 mark for correct
information in the table)*

3 a) 185 − 75 − 50 =

Bid amount	Number of bids made
Less than £50	50
£50 to £100	75
More than £100	**60**
Totals:	185

(1 mark)

b) 75 + 60
= **135 bids** *(1 mark)*
You could also work this out
by doing 185 − 50.

c) 7 + 12 = 19 items sold
for less than £100.

```
    1 9
×   1 7
  1 3₆3
+ 1 9 0
  3 2 3
    1
```

So Mo will donate **£323**.
Yes — he is correct.
*(1 mark for a correct
method of multiplying
17 × 19, 1 mark for
£323, 1 mark for the
correct conclusion
with working)*

Section Four:
Mixed Practice

Test 1 — pages 52 and 53

1 **9:20 am** *(1 mark)*

2 **F. Miller** *(1 mark)*

3 **310 km** *(1 mark)*

4
```
      3 4
×   1 7
    2 3₂8
+ 3 4 0
    5 7 8
```

So Jake charges **£578**.
*(1 mark for a correct
method of multiplying
34 × 17, 1 mark for the
correct answer)*

5 a)
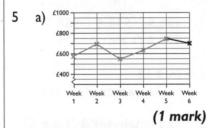
(1 mark)

b) **Week 3** *(1 mark)*
Jake earned £550 in
Week 3.

c) **3 weeks** *(1 mark)*
They were Weeks 2, 5
and 6.

Test 2 — pages 54 and 55

1   *(1 mark)*

The first three shaded faces are
squares or rectangles, which
each have four right angles.

2 $\frac{1}{4}$ *(1 mark)*

3 £5 − £2.65
= **£2.35** *(1 mark)*

4 762 ÷ 12 = 63.5
So **£63.50** each month.
*(2 marks for the correct
answer, otherwise 1 mark
for 762 ÷ 12 = 63.5)*
You must use the correct money
format. You wouldn't get the
second mark for £63.5.

5 a) 13:00 → 13:21 is
21 minutes *(1 mark)*
You'd get the same answer
using the correct times from
any other column.

b) Three buses arrive at Dean
Street before 14:00. The
bus that arrives at 13:51
has no wheelchair ramp.
So she wants the bus that
arrives at 13:36. This bus
leaves Applegate at **13:15**.
*(2 marks for the correct
answer, otherwise
1 mark for identifying
the bus that arrives
at 13:36)*

Test 3 — pages 56 and 57

1   **a teaspoon** *(1 mark)*

2   **£2.30** *(1 mark)*

3   **13 cm** *(1 mark)*
    You must include units with
    your answer to get the mark.

4   a)

Strength	Frequency
1.50	**4**
2.00	**2**
2.50	**3**
3.00	**6**

(1 mark)

   b) $\frac{7}{10}$ *(1 mark)*

5   1 km = 1000 m
    21 × 47 m = 987 m
    987 m is less than 1000 m.
    No — Aamir is wrong.
    *(1 mark for 987 m, 1 mark
    for comparing with 1 km,
    1 mark for the correct
    conclusion with working)*

Test 4 — pages 58 and 59

1   **three hundred and
    fifty-two pounds and
    twenty pence** *(1 mark)*

2   ⬡ and ⬡ *(1 mark)*

3   260 ÷ 1000
    = **0.26 litres** *(1 mark)*

4   150 g ÷ 5 = **30 g**
    *(2 marks for the correct
    answer, otherwise 1 mark
    for a correct method of
    finding one fifth)*

5   a) Add 0.15 L to get from
       one capacity to the next.
       0.65 + 0.15
       = **0.8 L** *(1 mark)*

   b) The bottle contains 350 ml.
      500 ml − 350 ml = **150 ml**
      *(2 marks for the correct
      answer, otherwise
      1 mark for evidence
      of reading 350 ml
      off the bottle)*

Test 5 — pages 60 and 61

1   **536.5   536.6   536.7
    537.6** *(1 mark)*

2   24 + 12
    = **36 games** *(1 mark)*

3   **22 remainder 8** *(1 mark)*

4   a) E.g.

Player	Games played	Cost (£ millions)
1	562	6.95
2	652	7.95
3	698	7.39
4	599	6.89

*(1 mark for a suitable
table format, 1 mark for
correct information in
the table)*

   b) **£7.95 million** *(1 mark)*
      Player 2 is the
      most expensive.

   c) Most games played:
      698 (by Player 3).
      Least games played:
      562 (by Player 1).
      Difference = 698 − 562
                 = **136 games**
      *(2 marks for the correct
      answer, otherwise
      1 mark for using the
      correct two numbers
      of games played)*